MAGIC MOMENTS

Edited By Jenni Harrison

First published in Great Britain in 2022 by:

Young Writers
Remus House
Coltsfoot Drive
Peterborough
PE2 9BF
Telephone: 01733 890066
Website: www.youngwriters.co.uk

Printed and bound in the UK by BookPrintingUK
Website: www.bookprintinguk.com
YB0493H

FOREWORD

For Young Writers' latest competition This Is Me,
we asked primary school pupils to look inside
themselves, to think about what makes them unique,
and then write a poem about it! They rose to the
challenge magnificently and the result is this fantastic
collection of poems in a variety of poetic styles.

Here at Young Writers our aim is to encourage creativity
in children and to inspire a love of the written word, so
it's great to get such an amazing response, with some
absolutely fantastic poems. It's important for children to
focus on and celebrate themselves and this competition
allowed them to write freely and honestly, celebrating
what makes them great, expressing their hopes and
fears, or simply writing about their favourite things.
This Is Me gave them the power of words. The result
is a collection of inspirational and moving poems that
also showcase their creativity and writing ability.

I'd like to congratulate all the young poets
in this anthology, I hope this inspires them
to continue with their creative writing.

CONTENTS

Qasim Ali (7)	59
Grace Thackeray (7)	60
Pawel Topa Letras (8)	61
Calum Brown (8)	62
Alex Head (7)	63
Sami Benkhelfallah (9)	64
Tabitha Faithful (8)	65
Eliza Sophia Powell (8)	66
Kara Chubb (7)	67
Sophie McGregor (8)	68
Isla Smith (8)	69
Daisy Ingham (8)	70
Toby Waine (9)	71
Hailey Chow Wing Kiu (9)	72
Riya Panchal (9)	73
Freddie Higgs (8)	74
Vintila Keragala (8)	75

St Margaret Mary RC Primary School, Erdington

Meghan D'sa (10)	76
Nathan Alem (9)	78
Chimamanda Aninweze (9)	79
Solyana Berhiu (9)	80
Zac Ashwin (9)	82
Caleb Millwood Martin (10)	83
Renee Mcloughlin (8)	84
Zara Ntui (9)	86
Melael Aklilu (9)	87
Caiden Tran (9)	88
Sophie Hudson (9)	89
Elizabeth Mendy (8)	90
Ryan Price (9)	91
Grace Millwood Martin (9)	92
Zion Carby Gordon (9)	93
Chisom Egboh (9)	94
Naziah Bailey (9)	95
Cleo Kent (8)	96
Sueellen O'Donoghue (9)	97
Katrina Dzene (8)	98
Leila Matingou (8)	99
Ruby Fahy (8)	100
Maya Cebula (8)	101

Jamel Daniels-Harborne (8)	102
Karina Marciniak (8)	103
Ava Rae Ward (10)	104
Oscar Was (8)	105
Natania Elias (8)	106
Natalie Kola (9)	107
Nadia Wajnert (8)	108
Beulah Iyire (9)	109
Aayat Jamshaid (9)	110
Pru Coney (9)	111
Nevaeh Mclonghlin (9)	112
Hope Elizabeth Marie Thompson (8)	113
Adel Msampha (9)	114
Ocean Flower Hemmings (8)	115
Violet Wesley (10)	116
Daniel Wright (9)	117
Timi Bello (8)	118
Zofia Poplawska (8)	119
Isabelle Mekonnen (8)	120
Dominik Michalowski (8)	121
Pius Rejo (8)	122
Liliana Szczawinska (10)	123
Nieshawn De Loyola (9)	124
Lewis Roberts (9)	125
Ymad Yankam (9)	126
Ava Mombeini (9)	127
Tiana May Carla McSharry (9)	128
Esrom Solomon (9)	129
Maria Chinyere (9)	130
Jos-Jordan Febeolisa Ohagwu (9)	131
Makomborero Mambo (9)	132
Valentina Stokes Aston (9)	133
Jessica Nicholls (8)	134
Shay Ward (10)	135
Eugenie Diouf (8)	136
Amélie McKenna (8)	137
Ugonna Onyiuke (9)	138
Kaitlyn Dunne (8)	139
Ava Allen (9)	140
Elidana Ablelom (8)	141
Charlotte Mae Ogrady (9)	142
Grayson Marklew (8)	143

Rico Joseph (8)   144
Logan Downey (8)   145
Bryan Macznik (8)   146
Mason Rendell   147

St Monica's RC Primary School, Flixton

Jamil Maou (8)   148
Theo Cheung (8)   149
Darla Roberts Fitzpatrick (8)   150
Scarlett Allen (8)   151
Leo Kennedy (8)   152
Ronan Leigton (7)   153
Ava Rawson (7)   154
Faith Boardwell (10)   155

Wellfield Methodist & Anglican Church School, Burnley

Ruby Riding (9)   156
Rylee Hoban (9)   157
Hannah Reid (9)   158
Seb Smith (9)   159
Sosha Derbyshire (9)   160
Joseph Dickson (9)   161
Jessica Ashworth (9)   162
Riley Richardson (9)   163
Jessie Madden (9)   164
Finley Danson (9)   165
Lydia Gibson (9)   166
Georgia-May Mawson (9)   167
Mimi Cedillo (9)   168
Logan Meades (9)   169
Keegan Macrae (9)   170
Finnigan Walton (9)   171
Reo Taylor (10)   172

Winterbourne Boys' Academy, Thornton Heath

Micah Williams (10)   173
Raees Auzine (10)   174

THE POEMS

This Is Me

My name is Mairi,
It might sound weird to some,
But to me, it sounds beautiful.
Some people call me adventurous Mairi,
I love that name because it resembles me a lot.
Sometimes I cry,
But that does not make me weak,
It makes me try harder.
When people are mean to me,
I ignore them,
They soon stop.
I am very kind-hearted,
I have a lot of friends.
That is what makes me different,
That's what makes me Mairi.

Mairi Scotson (9)
Aldourie Primary School, Aldourie

Harris

H appier than a winning team,
A s grand as a digger.
R eally as big as a spade,
R eally fearless.
I 'm as grand as a dog,
S illy as a bird.

F antastically friendly,
R aptors I don't like.
A s on as a light switch,
S ensible as a parent.
E very time on task.
R esponsible.

Harris James Fraser (9)
Aldourie Primary School, Aldourie

This Is Emylou

My name is Emylou,
It might be different.
I like skateboarding,
I am a girl that skateboards.
But that's what makes me, me.
I am as adventurous as a porpoise,
And that's what makes me, me.
I am the sun,
I sparkle like the snow.
I will never change because I am Emylou.
The breeze blows through my hair,
I am lightning.

Emylou Krall-Delagrave (9)
Aldourie Primary School, Aldourie

Never Give Up

I might cry but that doesn't mean I give up.
I might be young but I am brave.
I am not as shiny as a diamond,
I am not as beautiful as a butterfly,
But I am still beautiful in my own way.
I am shy but creative.
I am a shooting star.
This is me and no one can change who I am.

Zara Foster (8)
Aldourie Primary School, Aldourie

Riding Across The Sky

I feel so free, like sailing across the sky.
My heart is racing on and on.
I want to have this feeling forever.
My hand brushes against his blowing mane.
It makes my heart happy.

Klara Gehrke (9)
Aldourie Primary School, Aldourie

Who I Am?

I am who I am,
I might not be the most beautiful,
But I have beauty in full.
I might not be your first choice,
But I am a great choice.
I am me.

And that's cool 'cause I am good at being myself,
And me.
I don't care about anything you say about me,
It's just that you're not as good as me.
To everyone out there, there is a better way of
looking at your critics,
Tell them you are not what they say, say to
yourself,
"I'm the best ever, I'm a legend."
Remember, confession is possession!

Maliha Mahmood (11)
Alexandra Park Junior School, Oldham

A Day In My School Life

I wake up and feel,
Something happening.
I have a scrumptious meal,
And I think I'm still imagining.

I go to school and play with my friends,
And I try not to be rough,
I try not to offend,
Even if things are still tough.

I get back home and I'm tired,
But I have to study.
I drift to sleep,
And finish it as it's required.

Leah Nuri (11)
Alexandra Park Junior School, Oldham

This Is Me

Z ara is my name.
A yar is my baby brother.
R iding my orange and black bike is fun.
A pples are my favourite fruit.

Y ummy yoghurt is the best.
A untie's house I love to go to.
S weets and chocolates I love eating.
I nsects I run away from.
N umbers are a little tricky, but I always do my best.

Zara Yasin (7)
Alexandra Park Junior School, Oldham

All About Me

You are who you are,
Just like me.
I can run,
I am fast as,
A flash,
Can you?
I am very pretty,
Are you very pretty?
Sometimes I go to the park, do you too?
Do you go to Spain every year, well I do?
Do you have glasses? Well I do if you don't.
This is a poem from Iman.

Iman Ahmed (7)
Alexandra Park Junior School, Oldham

This Is Me

I am caring,
I like sharing.
I am nice,
And give great advice.

Flowers are colourful,
And very wonderful.
I love school,
Because it's cool.

I promise,
I will always be honest.
I am brilliant,
And resilient.

Ameera Yaseen (11)
Alexandra Park Junior School, Oldham

I Love My Hair

My name is Husna,
I have really long black hair,
Everyone tells me to cut it,
But I really don't care.
It's curly and frizzy and it goes everywhere,
But I have to say again,
I really love my black, frizzy, curly hair.

Husna Jamall (8)
Alexandra Park Junior School, Oldham

About Me!

Hi, I'm Margot loud and true,
I try my best, how 'bout you?

Enough from you,
Now focus on me,
I like sloths,
They are proud and free.

I love dogs too,
Can't forget 'em, they're just too cute.
They keep me sane,
Please don't forget them!

At first glance, I'm quite tall and different,
But soft spots,
I have, yeah, quite a lot of them.

My, oh the time has flown,
Look at you, please don't groan,
Oh, hope you enjoyed the show!

Margot Storey (9)
Lawford CE (VA) Primary School, Lawford

Salt And Pepper

S alt is one of my rats, let me tell you about her.
A lways hungry,
L et her eat!
T akes Pepper's food, so sad.

A mazing rats!
N aughty and cheeky,
D etermined to escape for fun.

P epper is one of my rats, let me tell you about her.
E ats so cute.
P eeps her claws through the cage.
P eople say Pepper is cuter than Salt.
E very day I see her waiting for me.
R at poem I love and I love rats.

Isabella Jones (9)
Lawford CE (VA) Primary School, Lawford

My Lovely Dog

T he great Penny you are.
H er fur is great.
I love her and she loves me,
S he loves treats.

I love her and she loves me,
S he and me are perfect buddies.

M e and my dog love colours.
Y ou love wildlife like me.

G ood dog,
O h, you are,
O h, you are,
D ogs are great.

D ogs like you,
O h, amazing dog,
G ood dog you are.

Evelyn Gadsby (9)
Lawford CE (VA) Primary School, Lawford

Me Me Me!

Me and Fretty the guitar,
In our police car.
Fretty was reading the Beano,
I was drinking a cappuccino.
Then we saw a criminal afar.

He jumped out of his car,
And tried to rob the bar.
He liked Harry Potter,
He was a big rotter.
So we put him behind big bars.

Me and Fretty had a cup of tea,
With Grant, my small matey.

We all like pizza,
And a big spotty cheetah.
This is the story of me!

Herbie Connell (10)
Lawford CE (VA) Primary School, Lawford

All About Me

A ll about me,
L ikes chocolate,
L ikes pasta.

A little thing about me is that I have a brother, mum, dad and dogs.
B roccoli and beans I hate,
O ctopus is my least favourite animal.
U ses a lot of electronics,
T he most thing I like to do is sleep.

M argot is my best friend,
E velyn is my funniest friend.

Naomi Cox (10)
Lawford CE (VA) Primary School, Lawford

This Is Me

T his me, yes that is correct,
H ide-and-seek, playing to the best.
I like to eat pizza, now that's more me,
S crambling eggs while watching TV.

I don't think I'm slow, now that's not a guess,
S o race me to prove that I'm the best.

M e and my dogs playing new games,
E ating ice and making some names.

Travis Coward (9)
Lawford CE (VA) Primary School, Lawford

World War Two

W hen war starts, chaos is here.
O ut, out of crumbling buildings 'cause of the blitz.
R etreat, retreat when the enemy push forward.
L oud panzers fire their shells.
D eath, death all you find.

W ar is horrible, this one is six years long.
A sight for it to stop.
R ubble is all that is left in Berlin in 1945.

Edward Ford (9)
Lawford CE (VA) Primary School, Lawford

This Is Me!

M ia Lyons, yes that's me,
I love to draw and run free.
A nd to play and read and write,

L oving art and nature and a moonlit night!
Y ikes, I like sun and snow, but a tornado, no, no, no!
O h my, I haven't realised the time,
N ow I've got to go!
S ee you soon, I hope you liked the show!

Mia Lyons (10)
Lawford CE (VA) Primary School, Lawford

This Is Me!

I like drawing, what about you?
I know I'm not great but let's keep going,
Let's draw and paint, that's where I'm going.

Let's take a break.
I cannot wait to keep going,
My time is up so I hope,
You liked the show.
I cannot forget the best bit of the show, it's a...
Torpedo!

Abigail Tuner (10)
Lawford CE (VA) Primary School, Lawford

This Is Me

F ortnite all the way,

O ctopuses are my favourite animal,

R oblox is one of my favourite games,

T NT from Minecraft,

N arwhales are in a cold place,

I once built an igloo as big to fit me, I went inside,

T ogether forever, me and my friends,

E very day I am here.

Lily Pentney (9)
Lawford CE (VA) Primary School, Lawford

I Am Me

T ry hard!
H appy!
I ndependent
S assy!

I ntelligent!
S pecial!

M otivated!
E xcellent!

R eally cool,
O h my gosh, I'm amazing,
S trong,
I nto a lot of things,
E nergised.

Rosie Newman (10)
Lawford CE (VA) Primary School, Lawford

Books I Like!

B ox up some books,

O ff to the island.

O n the sea a,

K ind of king,

S erves all the boxes.

I n hope to find,

L ove in the,

I sland's secrets a,

K ind of peace hidden within,

E xcept he has not found it!

Poppy Turner (10)

Lawford CE (VA) Primary School, Lawford

About Me!

I like football,
Football is great.
I am a left midfielder,
I love football.

Dogs are amazing,
They're soft and cuddly,
And great to hug,
They cheer you up,
I love dogs.

I love cricket,
It's great,
The satisfaction of batting the ball is amazing.

Thomas Oakley (9)
Lawford CE (VA) Primary School, Lawford

My Dream House

One thousand rooms,
Everything looms.
Thirty maids,
Want to be paid.
Fifty pools,
No rules.

A massive party,
The food is tarty.
Always friends,
On the weekends.

Lots of pets,
Tennis nets.
Lots of TVs,
Attracting bees.
Happy me.

Sophia Sparling (9)
Lawford CE (VA) Primary School, Lawford

This Is Me

I am Emma,
Cucumber and chocolate,
Poodles and noodles,
That's me!
Games and planes,
Books and wolves,
That's me!
Arts and smarts,
Green and jumpsuits,
That's me!
Sometimes I get angry, my head explodes into
colours!
That's me!

Emma Gooding (9)
Lawford CE (VA) Primary School, Lawford

All About Me

This is a story all about me,
And how I play and cheer with glee.
All about the things I know,
Like I like to play with others too!
And you may have already got a clue,
That I am gonna play it soon.
Anyways, thanks for reading,
Thanks for reading, goodbye!

Josie Jammeh (10)
Lawford CE (VA) Primary School, Lawford

Why I Want To Be A Vet

I want to be a vet,
Because I love animals.
I love them,
I want to help them have the best lives they
possibly can.

Since I can remember,
I have always dreamt of curing them and saving
them,
And that is why I want to be a vet.

Ava Smith (9)
Lawford CE (VA) Primary School, Lawford

Colchester United!

Colchester United football team,
To play for them would be my dream.
Football is my favourite sport,
But it's not played on a basketball court.
Whenever I play matches,
My goalie is so good he does lots of catches.

Grant Thornton (9)
Lawford CE (VA) Primary School, Lawford

All My Food

A ll my food,
B roccoli and meat,
O ranges and peach,
U rchin from the sea,
T omatoes and tea.

M acaroni cheese,
E ggs and beef.

Sadie Wheatley (9)
Lawford CE (VA) Primary School, Lawford

Gamer

Whether pixels or cars,
Or animated stars.
Travelling through caves and caverns,
And noisy taverns.
I'm all in,
I'll do it all,
And that's not a sin!

Grace Travers (9)
Lawford CE (VA) Primary School, Lawford

All About Me!

A rt is a passion,
R insed brush tips,
T his is what I long for,
I n my adult life,
S o,
T hat dream I shall pursue.

Owain Lee (9)
Lawford CE (VA) Primary School, Lawford

All About Me

I like running and jumping.
I dislike mushrooms and cabbage.
I like cats but I dislike bats.
I like Nintendo Switch but not Minecraft.
I like touching slime but not green lime.
When I'm older I want to be an artist.
My goal is to score a goal between the poles.
I dislike space but I like to chase.
I like the diamond rings but I dislike the loud ping!
My dream is to be a famous singer.
I also like going to the playground,
But I dislike falling to the ground.
Dream high if you want to reach the sky.

Madison Fischer (7)
Sayes Court Primary School, Addlestone

All About Me!

I like touching slime but not red, blue and lime.
I like ice cream but not ice lollies.
I like chocolate pancakes but not butter pancakes.
I also like singing and dancing as much as playing
Monopoly and Ludo.
My dream was to have a swing but not a sting.
I like eating chocolate and lollies.
I don't like running and football but,
I like jumping on the trampoline.
I don't like boys, they are annoying.

Mishal Usman (7)
Sayes Court Primary School, Addlestone

Riddle

I am shy but really shy.
I have a brother in Chertsey High.
I am scared of the dark and I never sleep.
I never need help with too much work.
I have brown hair and it never curls and it is very hard to put it in a bun and ponytail.
I used to go to ballet but I needed to quit on my birthday to come here.
It already turned night-time when I got home.

Who am I?

Answer: I am me!

Sophia Danishvar (8)
Sayes Court Primary School, Addlestone

The Adventures Of Peyton

T he day I was born I loved spending time with my family.

H appy is the feeling that I am the most.

I am a helpful young lad.

S ayes Court is the school I have spent most of my life at.

I t has been hard work but now I am extremely smart!

S ocial is what I hope to be.

M y parents are better than you could wish for!

E nergy is what I am.

Peyton Okoro (11)

Sayes Court Primary School, Addlestone

All About Me

I like school,
But sometimes I would jump in my swimming pool,
Because it's relaxing.
I like tigers that can roar,
But I don't like giraffes that can't get through the door.
I dream that I will get puppies and horses,
But I don't like slugs and bugs.
I like dancing in the school hall,
My goals are football.
But I would like to play with my toys,
Instead of the boys.

Olivia Channell (7)
Sayes Court Primary School, Addlestone

My Favourite Animal

It has sharp teeth,
They climb like squirrels,
They're really majestic,
Their skin can be bright orange,
Most common in the rainforest.

Their canines chop through meat,
Devour everything head to feet.
These creatures are carnivores,
All they do is hunt for food.
They are not scavengers,
They eat freshly hunted.

What are they?
Jaguar.

Samuel Weston (10)
Sayes Court Primary School, Addlestone

All About Me!

I like handwriting,
But my brother would rather do scribbling.

I would sing in a band,
But not like people whose voice is bad.

I don't like creepy clown dreams,
I would rather like dreams about me in a tree.
I like puppies but not a dog,
They bark so loudly they make my eardrums drop.
I like McDonald's but not ones that have yucky
food.

Elisa Saeidi (7)
Sayes Court Primary School, Addlestone

This Is Me

T he eyes I have are blue,

H ave you got a pet? I do.

I s today Sunday? Wait, no, Monday, I am so forgetful.

S hopping and eating are my favourite things.

I s my hair a mix or a blonde? I have no idea.

S he is my mum and he is my dad.

M y brain is like mathematics,

E ven though I hate reading.

Laura Ozola (9)

Sayes Court Primary School, Addlestone

This Is Me

Some people know me as extremely friendly,
Others know me as very funny.
I like netball,
As I love playing with a ball.
I am a ray of sunshine, depending on the hour.
I am an artist whose creations vary,
My artwork I make extraordinary.
I love to sing, loudly,
My mother tells me to sing quietly.
I get nervous when the teacher calls my name.

Olivia Frimpong (10)
Sayes Court Primary School, Addlestone

All About Me

I like puppies, kittens, rabbits,
But I dislike spiders and I like dolphins, fish and otters.
I dislike mushrooms, lettuce and green Brussel sprouts.
My dream is to be a carrot,
Because I like the taste and the colour.
My dream is to be a baker at a cafe.
My goal is to be a famous baker in the world.
My dream is to live in the countryside.

Eleanor (7)
Sayes Court Primary School, Addlestone

All About Me

I dislike slime but I like to rhyme.
I like to score goals between the poles.
I don't like giraffes that can't get through the door.
I like space as much as I like to chase.
I like to read but I don't like to flee.
I like bees but I don't like keys.
If you don't dream high, you won't reach the sky.

Rori Taylorson (8)
Sayes Court Primary School, Addlestone

All About Me

I like dancing but I do not like singing.
I would like to be a famous gymnastic person when
I grow up.
I like Christmas but I don't like Halloween,
Because it is too spooky for me.
I love my family but sometimes they can be
annoying.
I have seven rings and they ping.
I love playing with balls but not with boys.

Sienna Machicado (8)
Sayes Court Primary School, Addlestone

All About Me

I like scoring goals between the poles.
I like Harry Kane, he never gets in pain.
I like cats but not bats.
I like cakes but my mom always bakes.
I like crops, later my mom always drops.
I like karate and in January I have a party.
When I go to Spain I don't get in pain.
I like food, some people be rude.

Jake Skinner (7)
Sayes Court Primary School, Addlestone

All About Me

I like switches but not glitches.
I like football but not netball.
I like bats but not cats.
I don't like rings but I like swings.
I like tigers but not fires.
I don't like unicorns but I like dragons.
I don't like Peppa Pig but I like Pokémon.
I like loud roars but not silly doors.

Joshua (8)
Sayes Court Primary School, Addlestone

This Is My Wonderful Self

T he game called football is my favourite.
H arry Potter is the coolest.
I am not shy.
S piders are creepy to me.

I love dogs and monkeys.
S pider-Man is the best for me.

M oose I've never seen,
E veryone is one year younger than me.

Ricardo Dasilva (10)
Sayes Court Primary School, Addlestone

This Is Me!

T all in height,
H owever, I dislike the night.
I love turtles,
S ince I have one that's purple (stuffed toy).

I am a patient person,
S ometimes I am not.

M y name is Lia,
E ven though it's not my first.

Patricia DeSousa (9)
Sayes Court Primary School, Addlestone

My Riddle

I am funny and I am smart.
I like rugby but I am not a boy.
I love candy and I love cats.
I have golden hair.
I am from Singapore.
I love ballet.
I have three cats.
I love otters.
I love dogs and puppies.

Who am I?

Answer: Abigail.

Abigail Pigot (8)
Sayes Court Primary School, Addlestone

What Is My Favourite Animal?

It is small but swift,
Black and white with a hint of pink.
But it is loud,
And mostly hungry,
It is small and fluffy,
And can sometimes be naked.
They are good as house pets but mostly wild,
Can you guess what it is?

Answer: A guinea pig.

Aidan Liddle (10)
Sayes Court Primary School, Addlestone

Carrots!

I dislike carrots so I...
Kick them,
Flick them,
Grab them,
Stab them,
Sheesh-kebab them,
Punch them,
Crunch them,
Knockdown-punch them,
Attack them,
Smack them,
Burn them,
Turn them,
Defeat them,
But never eat them!

Dylan Brown (10)
Sayes Court Primary School, Addlestone

All About Me

I like scoring football goals between some poles,
I also like playing lots of computer games.
I dislike doing homework all day,
I also dislike lots of onions.
My goal is to play basketball very well,
My dream is to win against Harry Kane in a
football match.

Oliver Trafford (7)
Sayes Court Primary School, Addlestone

This Is Me

T all and skinny,
H ave a big brain.
I like maths and reading.
S ea is my favourite place to be.

I love my family.
S uperstar singer.

M y favourite subject is art.
E vie is my sister.

Rosie Akass (9)
Sayes Court Primary School, Addlestone

My Favourite Animal Riddle

They are fast like the wind,
They don't roar, they squeak.
They trip their prey like a joker,
They have spots like midnight.
They digest as fast as they run,
They are the third biggest cat.
What are they?

Answer: A cheetah.

Harrison Bacon (9)
Sayes Court Primary School, Addlestone

This Is Me

I like basketball.
I like the Ferrari car.
I like broccoli.
I like tarantulas.
I don't like the moon.
I like computer games.
I like to run.
I like pool.
I don't like carrots.
I don't like giraffes.
I like football.

Yusuf Islam (7)
Sayes Court Primary School, Addlestone

All About Me

I like baking so I baked a cake.
I like playing football with my cousin.
My goal is to beat my cousin in football.
I dislike my mum waking me up in the morning.
If you don't dream high, you won't reach the sky.
I like dancing in the hall.

Olivia Huff (7)
Sayes Court Primary School, Addlestone

All About Me

I dislike spiders but I do like tigers.
I like queens but I don't like kings.
I like lions that have a roar,
But I don't like giraffes that can't fit through the door.
I have a slope,
But I can't use a skipping rope.

Amaiya (7)
Sayes Court Primary School, Addlestone

All About Me

I love horses but I don't like slugs.
My dream is to be in a bing bang bong.
I like cats but I don't like slugs.
My dream is to become a zookeeper, once I'm older.
If you don't dream high then you won't reach the sky.

Maisie Martin (7)
Sayes Court Primary School, Addlestone

All About Me

I love dinosaurs as well as Harry Potter,
I don't like to mutter.
I think to myself, is my imagination cool?
I like to build with tools.
Also, I like myself,
My friends know what's best,
Also, the worst is a pest.

Qasim Ali (7)
Sayes Court Primary School, Addlestone

All About Me

I like swimming but I don't like football,
I like dancing in the school hall.
What I like most is playing with my toys,
But I don't like playing with the boys.
If you don't dream high,
You won't reach the sky.

Grace Thackeray (7)
Sayes Court Primary School, Addlestone

Who Am I?

I am funny and smart, shy but brave.
I am a good judoka and I have a German shepherd guard.
I slither through books like a snake.
I have as much hair as a dog, but only on my head.
As strong as a lion but afraid of the dark.

Pawel Topa Letras (8)
Sayes Court Primary School, Addlestone

Charlie

I'm as silly as a monkey.
I have a dog called Lilly.
I have some glasses.
I'm a pro gamer.
I'm a pro climber.
My favourite colour is red.

Who am I?

Answer: Charlie.

Calum Brown (8)
Sayes Court Primary School, Addlestone

About Me

I don't like long stuff,
Because I always get it wrong.
I like to bake because I can bake a cake.
I like to take cake from the kitchen,
Because I like it.
I have a cat that is always on my mat.

Alex Head (7)
Sayes Court Primary School, Addlestone

Who Am I?

My dream is to be a footballer.
I play video games,
And I like biking.
I like playing outside with my friends.
I like sour and spicy food.
I have an office.
I am a bit funny.
I have three sisters.

Sami Benkhelfallah (9)
Sayes Court Primary School, Addlestone

Who Am I?

I've got brown fluffy hair like a cat.
I'm as brave as a lion.
I fly high in the sky like a fairy.
In my heart, the sun always shines bright.
I'm as sweet as a cupcake.

Who am I?

Tabitha Faithful (8)
Sayes Court Primary School, Addlestone

Football And Games

I love football.
I don't play for a team.
I support Arsenal and Chelsea.
I go to my park and play football.
I have a Nintendo and I play Animal Crossing on it.

Answer: Elica.

Eliza Sophia Powell (8)
Sayes Court Primary School, Addlestone

All About Me

I like strawberries but not berries.
I like cats but not bats.
I like banana but not papaya.
I want to be a dog carer
I like netball but not football.
I like Harry Potter but not to mutter.

Kara Chubb (7)
Sayes Court Primary School, Addlestone

Riddle

I am as shy as a cat.
I have brown hair like a fuzzy bear.
I am as sweet as candy.
I am as bright as the sun.
I am soft as a cloud.

Who am I?

Answer: I am me!

Sophie McGregor (8)
Sayes Court Primary School, Addlestone

Who Am I?

I score hoops like a professional player.
I am as smart as a teacher.
I run like a bull.
I like to swim in a pool.
I am as kind as a cupcake.
Who am I?

Answer: Isla.

Isla Smith (8)
Sayes Court Primary School, Addlestone

The Middle Riddle

I like playing games,
I'm as kind as a butterfly.
I like making crafts as fast as a lion,
I like running as fast as a leopard.

Who am I?

Answer: Daisy.

Daisy Ingham (8)
Sayes Court Primary School, Addlestone

This Is Me!

I am,
Kinda slow mind,
A fast runner,
Good reader,
Not really a football fan.

I am tall, helpful, shy,
Tidy at school I'm,
Not really a talker.

Toby Waine (9)
Sayes Court Primary School, Addlestone

Who Am I...

I'm fast like a leopard.
I like to wear dresses.
I like animals.
I don't have any sisters or brothers.
Who am I?

Answer: Hailey.

Hailey Chow Wing Kiu (9)
Sayes Court Primary School, Addlestone

Riddle

I am as shy as a bird,
I have black hair.
I shine as bright as the sun,
I am kind.

Who am I?

Answer: Myself.

Riya Panchal (9)
Sayes Court Primary School, Addlestone

Riddle

I am good at golf,
Good at basketball.
I have got a brother,
I am also good at rugby.

Who am I?

Answer: Freddie.

Freddie Higgs (8)
Sayes Court Primary School, Addlestone

Me

I am a footballer,
I am a computerist,
I am a gamer,
I am a Lego master.
This is me.

Who am I?

Vintila Keragala (8)
Sayes Court Primary School, Addlestone

Sadness

Sadness is like an enigma,
One minute you're okay,
The second your eyes are,
Flooding.

Being struck with anger?
Being left out?
Being a shadow to,
Someone,
Maybe even yourself.

You can only pour out,
The sadness, no one,
Can help when the dark comes.

But maybe someone,
Will help the darkness,
Pour out your soul,
And refill it,
With light.

Who knows?
A puzzle,
A sorrow,
Regret,
And trust.

If all you want,
Is to be filled with light,
Come join the people with sadness,
In the night.

Maybe they will help,
The ones with their problems,
But will they hide?
Or come back,
Reincarnation happens,
Or maybe sadness.

Meghan D'sa (10)
St Margaret Mary RC Primary School, Erdington

Football

F ootballers are very hard workers and earn a lot of money,

O verall, prefer football out of all sport.

O ut of all footballers, it's Rashford, who is a left-winger,

T all, handsome, fast and skilful.

B eing a footballer is very hard, you've got to be strong,

A ll footballers are good but Ronaldo is outstanding.

L eaving my school biased, hard, but Rashford made me happy.

L aws of football: no fouls, no fights, and no touching the ref.

E asy wins for Manchester United.

R ashford is really inspirational and I hope to be like him.

S aying I want to be a footballer is easy but showing it is hard.

Nathan Alem (9)

St Margaret Mary RC Primary School, Erdington

Spotlight On Me!

There I am backstage, waiting for my great
performance,
My heart is racing, I can feel the bump as if I have
crashed into a car.
I mutter a prayer as I get called onto the dark
stage,
For this may be my biggest moment.
I will always remember who I am,
And where I came from.
Ping!
The spotlight is on me,
I take my first step as the music swirls into me.
A jump, a leap,
A twist and a spin,
I really believe I'm going for gold!
The results are in,
My heart is thumping louder than ever before.
Woo!
I've won, I've won,
It's incredible what you can do when you try,
There I was, with the crowd roaring on.

Chimamanda Aninweze (9)

St Margaret Mary RC Primary School, Erdington

This Is Me

Generous, kind,
A super-fast mind.
Science is my power,
But maths makes me cower.

Shouting like a cobra,
Running like a Ferrari,
Barking like a dog,
Can't wait to get an autograph.

A jump, I sprint,
I'm a super lazy kid.
A lifelong football fan,
I go to matches whenever I can.

He's rich, he's a king,
We all praise him, that's right,
So you'll have to praise me too.

So this is me, mostly,
Sad, sometimes happy.
And bring my mood to a super quick end,

I rely on my gang,
And my lunatic friends!

Solyana Berhiu (9)

St Margaret Mary RC Primary School, Erdington

This Is Me

Z ap and zing are cool words,
A ll topics I like are English, science and sport.
C ool things are like Roblox,
H am is nice, I like it with rice,
A nd I like Roblox.
R asharn is my friend and Mason and Ryan.
Y ou never give up on life.

A ll food I like is pizza, Minecraft, I like games.
S inging is my least favourite thing.
H ow do I like pizza? Because it is nice to me.
W hat I like is pasta, breaded chicken.
I usually am angry and say, but mostly talking.
N ativity is my favourite movie.

Zac Ashwin (9)
St Margaret Mary RC Primary School, Erdington

My Poem Of History

Listen here kid, I'm gonna make history,
So you better listen to me.
So if you wanna be revolting,
You better know about Molten.
'Cause this is just the chorus,
So you're gonna want more of us.
So you better read this quick,
Or you're gonna be sick.
So my surname is Millwood-Martin,
But guys, I can't stop farting,
'Cause this matter isn't of laughing.
So if you want pain and suffering,
Eat a very poisonous muffin.
If you like work,
Get my hero called Emies quick.
So if you were separated,
You must know how to be levitating.

Caleb Millwood Martin (10)
St Margaret Mary RC Primary School, Erdington

Who I Am

I am a,
Poem writer,
A pet lover,
I love,
To eat.
I am a heavy sleeper,
I like to snuggle my kitten.
People say I'm tall,
My favourite animal is a kitten.
I have a sprinkle of happiness,
English is my superpower.
I have a dash of sadness,
But my mood can change as quick as a flash.
I make shows and I have the confidence of an actor,
My dream is to be an actor and a singer with my cousin.
I have an amazing imagination,
You wouldn't believe I love to dance and sing.

I can be crazy,
And I can be cheeky,
He, he!

Renee Mcloughlin (8)

St Margaret Mary RC Primary School, Erdington

When I'm Older

When I'm older I want to be famous,
But I'm just curious,
How do people make their dreams come true?
I'm just a girl, there's nothing special about me.
I wouldn't say I always say the truth.

Sometimes I'm afraid people won't like me,
So I hide myself and make different personalities,
To different people in my family.
Sometimes I'm nice, sometimes I'm rude, but in the end, I'm me,
Ordinary me,
But soon, I will be extraordinary.

When I'm older I want my parents to be proud of me,
Not disappointed in me.

Zara Ntui (9)
St Margaret Mary RC Primary School, Erdington

My Name

M elael, she's so gorgeous,

E asy really, life is really easy,

L ine, I'm the first in line, the place is mine,

A wesome, I'm awesome alright, I have friends that make me awesome, Suelleen, Zara and Pru.

E loquent I am always,

L ove your neighbour as you love yourself.

A lly, I want to live there,

K ing, I am the king of the world,

L ove always comes back to you,

I am the drama queen,

L ove you guys,

yo **U** lot are lovely always.

Melael Aklilu (9)
St Margaret Mary RC Primary School, Erdington

My Life

I am nice,
My favourite food is chicken and rice.
I'm nine years old,
I'm nine years old who has a funny personality,
And I'm nine years old with a good face.
I wouldn't have been here now,
If it wasn't for them,
I love my parents.
I'm always caring and sharing,
If it wasn't for my teacher Mrs Gibson,
She's a lovely teacher.
I'm funny and I got a lot of money,
I'm nice and I love Jesus Christ.
I am living a happy life because you taught me,
Mrs Gibson, thank you.

Caiden Tran (9)

St Margaret Mary RC Primary School, Erdington

Things All About Sophie

I love playing games and playing with my friends.
I love doing new things and being myself.
I love to share my things with my sister Isla.
Whenever I'm sad I go play with my cat Maddie,
And whenever I'm at school she misses me.
I love doing skipping and playing with friends,
especially my bestie TT.
I love to spend time with my cousins Renae, Macey
and Kacie.
My favourite animal is a cat.
My favourite things to do in my spare time are
gaming and visiting my Grandparents Nanny Ang,
Grandad Kev, Nanny Sue and Grandad Phil.

Sophie Hudson (9)
St Margaret Mary RC Primary School, Erdington

This Is Me

Kind, caring, lots of fun,
Loving, sweet, I'm a wonderful girl.
Up in my bed,
Writing poems to blow people away.
For a while, I saw a describing tree right in my
eyes,
And checked it out, just for a little while.
There I saw me,
Sitting in a tree,
Oh my gosh, it was describing me.
Kind, caring, lots of fun,
Loving, sweet, I'm a wonderful girl.
Butterflies swarming,
Ferraris vrooming,
There was me,
Sitting in the describing tree,
Waiting for another child to notice me.

Elizabeth Mendy (8)
St Margaret Mary RC Primary School, Erdington

Pain

Pain, pain, worst thing in life,
Sometimes you hurt at random times,
Sharp stabs like a knife,
Please forgive me for my painfully good rhymes.

Boom, when you least expect it,
Pain latches onto you,
Bam, like you fell in a pit,
With pain, you simply have to make do.

Screams from the cursed feeling,
All pains find them appealing.
Then, they disappear without a trace,
Then the victim never forgets the laughter,
From the look on their face.

Ryan Price (9)
St Margaret Mary RC Primary School, Erdington

All About Me

A fter school, I like to play with my friends.
L ove being helpful by helping people.
L ike cheering my friends up when they're sad.

A lways help my friends when they're hurt.
B eing creative all the time.
O verly friendly with friends.
U tterly boring towards my family.
T elling my friends how to do something.

M y favourite animal is a dog.
E veryone is the best in my family.

Grace Millwood Martin (9)

St Margaret Mary RC Primary School, Erdington

92

Happy Wishes Wash The Dishes

M om spent lots of money,
Y ou can all come to my party.

B irthdays are the best,
I love today,
R eally excited to open my present,
T he amount of presents I have is incredible.
H i guys is the first thing I said when I saw my friends,
D ad spent a lot of money, just not as much as Mom,
A lways get presents,
Y mad is my best friend and I'm certain he'll come.

Zion Carby Gordon (9)
St Margaret Mary RC Primary School, Erdington

This Is Me!

I love flowers, they are so fine,
People call me a copycat, I like to be mine.
I am myself and I like to be free,
So how do I do it? Just wait and see,

If you need a friend, I'll be here,
Even you don't want me near.
I like to dance,
What's one don't give a chance.

Lovely person, shining bright,
Someones got a golden light.
My friend, don't you see?
I will be there when you need me.

Chisom Egboh (9)
St Margaret Mary RC Primary School, Erdington

Two Sides Of Naziah

Hi, my name is Naziah,
And I'm not a liar,
I'm so good they had to put me in the choir.
I have a funny personality,
And I'm very cheeky chappy.
I don't like basketball because I'm not very tall,
But I do like to play football,
That's my favourite sport.
I have two sides to me,
And I love my family.
I'm a DJ on the side,
I've wanted to be one from young,
And my journey has just begun!

Naziah Bailey (9)

St Margaret Mary RC Primary School, Erdington

is Cleo,

ies,

S po... nnastics.

I am a girl,
S o what are you waiting for?

M y eyes are blue,
E veryone in school is unique.

C lever, calm and cool,
L oves life and especially glasses,
E veryone deserves my love and finally,
O vals are my favourite shape.

Cleo Kent (8)

St Margaret Mary RC Primary School, Erdington

All About Me And Feelings

I am nine years old,
Nine years old with kindness,
Nine years old, loving nature,
Nine years old, loves family obviously,
Nine years old who hopes to graduate high school,
Nine years old and loves school.

Kindness and caring,
Kindness and sharing,
Kindness and cheerful,
Kindness and angry... sometimes,
Kindness and caring,
Kindness and silly,
Kindness and funny,
Kindness and loud.

Sueellen O'Donoghue (9)
St Margaret Mary RC Primary School, Erdington

This Is Me!

To create me you will need:
A spoonful of helpfulness,
A can of creativity,
A glass of animal love,
Three teaspoons of adventure,
A ton of sparkles.

Now what you do:
Put some creativity in a bowl,
Three teaspoons of adventure,
And a ton of sprinkles,
Don't forget to add a spoonful of helpfulness,
And some animal love.
Cook it with love bubbles.

That's it, you have me!

Katrina Dzene (8)
St Margaret Mary RC Primary School, Erdington

This Is Me

I love to sketch, but my room,
Is a bit of a wreck,
My mom goes crazy if she sees a,
A little bit of a speck.
My favourite colour is yellow and it's better,
Not be better than me and my fellow.
Why are there bees swarming,
In the morning, while I'm in bed,
Yawning and yawning,
I hear one scream roaring and,
Roaring while I keep on,
Crawling, crawling.

What could that be!

Leila Matingou (8)
St Margaret Mary RC Primary School, Erdington

This Is Me

T alented at writing and reading,
H elpful at home, always on my phone,
I want to ride a horse, so let me please,
S inging songs might be a talent.

I 'm always talking, quite hard to stop,
S inging and sleeping, one of my things for sure.

M y lovely life is fun for sure, no need for more,
E loquent is how to describe my friends and I.

Ruby Fahy (8)
St Margaret Mary RC Primary School, Erdington

Maya Cake

To create me you will need:
A hop of excitement,
A sprinkle of joy,
One hundred millilitres of mischief,
A book full of happy vibes,
Twenty millilitres of happy vibes,
Twenty millilitres of musical notes.

Now you need to:
Put in a hop of excitement,
Mix it with a book of happy vibes,
Sprinkle joy and add musical notes!
Finally, stir in some mischief,
This is me!

Maya Cebula (8)
St Margaret Mary RC Primary School, Erdington

Jamel

J oyful and active and when others go and play with me I am joyful,

A nd I make lots of people laugh.

M any people enjoy my games and my creations.

E xcellent at gaming with people online.

L oving to others and family.

D one with all my homework, especially maths.

A nd I have a lot of family.

N ow come on, we got to go to holiday.

Jamel Daniels-Harborne (8)
St Margaret Mary RC Primary School, Erdington

This Is Me

A little box of games,
A chocolate cake,
A sprinkle of fun,
A dash of happiness,
A slither of mischief.

Now all you need to do is...
Mix in a cookie-filled bedroom,
Stir thoroughly.
Add a sprinkle of brightness,
Spread on a baking tray and cook until golden
brown.
Then slightly dust with icing sugar,
Allow to cool,
Then enjoy.
This is me.

Karina Marciniak (8)
St Margaret Mary RC Primary School, Erdington

All About Me!

Books are my favourite,
I could read them all day,
But I think that's enough,
Enough reading for today.

I love when my friends play with me,
I'm never lonely,
But I guess,
They're loyalty and holy.

I love my family,
Even if they're strict,
If someone asks, "Who's your favourite?"
I don't know who to pick.

Ava Rae Ward (10)
St Margaret Mary RC Primary School, Erdington

Me!

O nly one of me,
S ight like a skater,
C orrect my ways when I'm wrong,
A secret child,
R ecommend what I like.

W inner in my heart and home,
A BFF named Frank,
S omething special about me:

Kind, caring,
Speaking different languages,
Loyal, respecter,
Justice and,
Protective.

Oscar Was (8)
St Margaret Mary RC Primary School, Erdington

How To Make The Best Me

What you need:
A bag of love and cuteness,
A pinch of mischief,
A jar of reading,
A big bowl of creativity (flour).

How to make:
Get the big bowl of creativity,
Then pour the bag of love and cuteness,
And then add a pinch of mischief.
Finally, add the jar of reading,
Put in the oven and wait twenty minutes.
Then you made the best me!

Natania Elias (8)
St Margaret Mary RC Primary School, Erdington

Other Feelings

Sometimes, I feel joyful,
I play and dance around,
I feel like a shooting star,
I can spin myself around.

Sometimes I feel down,
I think in bed, sulking,
I feel like a fossil in the ground,
Then, I cannot sing.

Sometimes, I feel anger,
I kick and whack and cry,
I feel like I need some help,
I can be really shy.

Natalie Kola (9)
St Margaret Mary RC Primary School, Erdington

A Poem About Nadia

Hey, my name is Nadia.
My favourite animal is a horse,
My favourite hobby is horse riding,
I would ride horses all the time.
I would feed it until it's full,
I will also clean it, brush it, give it water, pick its hooves.
I would do everything to make sure it has a good owner.
When it's night I will put it in his stable and go to sleep.

Nadia Wajnert (8)
St Margaret Mary RC Primary School, Erdington

This Is Me And What I Like!

B aking with my family, especially their banana cakes.

E ntertaining my family and friends with jokes.

U sing my best skills when doing homework or making videos.

L oving and caring for my family and what they do.

A lways helping my friends if they need help to do something.

H elping with stuff around the house.

Beulah Iyire (9)

St Margaret Mary RC Primary School, Erdington

Me

I am wise and amazing,
I am clever and wise!
I am very tall and good,
We all can be amazing to live!

Live life, live life, enjoy yourself,
Live, live, live and life!
Enjoy your only life on earth,
Live!

I love the galaxy and its beauty,
I love unicorns!
Do what you want,
Live, live, live and live!

Aayat Jamshaid (9)
St Margaret Mary RC Primary School, Erdington

My Life

I love basketball,
It's the only sport I like,
All the others are kinda trash,
But this sport is kinda nice.

I'm the youngest in the class,
A little August baby,
It's kinda cool,
I'm a tiny little lady.

I hope to be an actress,
It is my biggest dream,
I am really sassy,
I am the sass queen.

Pru Coney (9)
St Margaret Mary RC Primary School, Erdington

The Story Of My Life

Hi, my name is Nevaeh,
I love the beach,
My favourite colour is baby blue,
I live with my mum,
I have one pet which is a hamster.

I have dark brown hair,
And brown eyes,
I'm kind and have two siblings,
I love school.

I love my family,
I am nine years old,
I love my mum,
And my siblings.

Nevaeh Mclonghlin (9)
St Margaret Mary RC Primary School, Erdington

What Makes Me Happy

What makes me happy is crafting because I'm
imaginative,
And I'm creative.
I have three favourite seasons,
They are called winter, autumn and spring.
I'm happy in the autumn breeze and the winter
freeze.
My birthday is in the month of May, the sixteenth.
My favourite animal is a bunny,
This is what makes me happy.

Hope Elizabeth Marie Thompson (8)
St Margaret Mary RC Primary School, Erdington

All About Me

My name is Adel and my favourite thing to do is
playing and doing work too,
Sometimes I like to play alone
And do drawing too.
But my favourite thing to really do
Is play with my crew.
Also what I hate the most,
Is doing maths and English too.
But last of all
What I despise the most
Is doing topics too.

Adel Msampha (9)
St Margaret Mary RC Primary School, Erdington

This Is Me! (Rap Version)

To be honest I'm a really good dancer,
I'm good at PE but it's boring to me.
I think that I will achieve stuff in my life,
I am smart, I am cool and I'm slick.
I could do basketball and I can do tumbling,
I'm not showing off by the way,
You can do stuff like me,
Because I believe in you!
Yasss!

Ocean Flower Hemmings (8)
St Margaret Mary RC Primary School, Erdington

About Me

My name is Violet,
I love the colour purple,
I live with my dad,
Cat and two guinea pigs!

I have brown hair,
And brown eyes,
My face is full of freckles,
And I am very pale.

I like to think I'm funny,
Good at drawing decently,
Smart and good at painting,
Though I can never tell.

Violet Wesley (10)
St Margaret Mary RC Primary School, Erdington

Me!

T iny in size,

H appy and kind,

I like to read and learn,

S easide is my favourite place to be.

I really love my family,

S ometimes make cakes.

M e and my friends have fun playing, they are great.

E lephants are funny because of their big floppy ears.

Daniel Wright (9)

St Margaret Mary RC Primary School, Erdington

This Is Me

This is me, quicker than a tiger, stronger than a
lion,
I'm the math king around here.
I'm really cool with my quick arms but,
When it comes to English I fall dead.
I'm angry but mostly happy,
I'm rich, I'm rich, give me the money.
It's time to disappear,
So it's time to say goodbye.

Timi Bello (8)
St Margaret Mary RC Primary School, Erdington

Loving Recipe

Twenty millilitres of musical notes,
One big chocolate cake,
Three served milkshakes,
Some crushed up cookies,
And some apples for health,
Two kilograms of kindness and beauty,
One kilogram of a loving family,
Three kilograms of love for family and friends,
Everything you need for a loving cake.

Zofia Poplawska (8)
St Margaret Mary RC Primary School, Erdington

This Is Me!

Hi, I'm Issy who's generous and kind,
I've got a big brain and a super-fast mind.
I'm mostly happy but sometimes can be grumpy,
To be honest, I think I'm the best out of the rest.
I have a big imagination and to bring bad moods
to an end,
I rely on my gang of lunatic friends.

Isabelle Mekonnen (8)
St Margaret Mary RC Primary School, Erdington

This Is Me!

I am a Roblox player,
A Fortnite player,
A Minecraft player,
I play with my friends,
I spend time with my mom,
I have a lot of games,
A big TV,
I have a lot of chocolate,
I am healthy,
Quick,
Tall,
Clever,
Cool,
Good,
And prophetic.

Dominik Michalowski (8)
St Margaret Mary RC Primary School, Erdington

Me!

T he best maths pupil,
H elping my dad shopping at the till.
I ncredible football striker,
S uper biker.

I nto a dash,
S ore on my leg and on my chest a rash.

M ad but really chatty,
E qually happy.

Pius Rejo (8)
St Margaret Mary RC Primary School, Erdington

Me And My Family And My Annoying Siblings

I like home, I like families,
But some families have kids.
I have siblings, but annoying siblings,
But I hang out with them a lot.
I like my mom and dad,
I am happy with my life,
But I am scared.
I like school, but still scared,
Help, please, I beg you.

Liliana Szczawinska (10)
St Margaret Mary RC Primary School, Erdington

My Life!

My life is like a book,
Anger or sweet,
But when it's my birthday,
My life gets another treat!
Cookies are ish but cake, now that's the one!
Going to school is always fun.
But at the end of the day, the lights come off,
And the shining moon comes.

Nieshawn De Loyola (9)
St Margaret Mary RC Primary School, Erdington

Emotional

Today is not my day,
It is an emotional day, I'm sorry,
I'm unhappy,
I can't make any friends,
'Cause I'm not popular anywhere I go,
But there's one person for me,
Who thinks I'm popular, you see,
My one and only,
My mom.

Lewis Roberts (9)
St Margaret Mary RC Primary School, Erdington

My Family

M um and Dad,
Y ou will have happiness towards them.

F amily is like my best friends,
A mazing and thoughtful,
M y supporters,
I nspiring,
L oving and caring,
Y ou can't live without them.

Ymad Yankam (9)
St Margaret Mary RC Primary School, Erdington

This Is Me

Hello, my name is Ava,
My favourite thing to do is drawing,
And my favourite food is mac and cheese,
And I am nine years old.
I have a brother,
He is three years old,
He is the best brother ever,
And I love my family because they're the best.

Ava Mombeini (9)
St Margaret Mary RC Primary School, Erdington

How To Make Me!

This is me and how to make me!
One hundred drops of happiness!
Two drops of sadness!
Fifty drops of tidiness!
Sixty drops of creativeness!
Long hair,
Eighty drops of funniness,
One hundred drops of kindness,
Seventy drops of helpfulness.

Tiana May Carla McSharry (9)
St Margaret Mary RC Primary School, Erdington

What Emotion Could I Be?

I stay inside all the time,
There is no time to go outside.
I have barely any friends,
But my parents' love never ends.
Who can save me from this despair?
Come to my house, I dare.

What emotion am I?

Answer: Angry.

Esrom Solomon (9)
St Margaret Mary RC Primary School, Erdington

Friends!

F riends are fun to play with,
R eally no one should be sad,
I think everyone can be friends,
E veryone can be kind!
N othing should stop us,
D oing kind things is good,
S aying good things is kind.

Maria Chinyere (9)
St Margaret Mary RC Primary School, Erdington

What Am I?

I have a,
Talent to eat but,
I'm not a human.
I can't control,
Myself and don't,
Blink.
I don't die, I,
Break and,
Can be,
Easily,
Rebuilt.

What am I?

Answer: A doll.

Jos-Jordan Febeolisa Ohagwu (9)
St Margaret Mary RC Primary School, Erdington

Who Am I?

I feel like an elf,
Not really myself.
I don't feel so kind,
Who am I?
Who am I? Just,
Don't want to die,
And that's no lie,
With everyone watching,
I feel a bit sly,
But for sure won't cry.

Makomborero Mambo (9)
St Margaret Mary RC Primary School, Erdington

Lonely Day

L ooking at the rainy window,
O nly the other children playing,
N obody has seen me yet,
E verybody else,
L earning to have fun on my own,
Y ou learn different things while being lonelier.

Valentina Stokes Aston (9)
St Margaret Mary RC Primary School, Erdington

Jessica

J oyful to play with my friends,
E ncouraging with my work,
S miling all day,
S mile, smile with my fabs,
I nspiring in my work,
C reative when I colour,
A ctive in my dancing.

Jessica Nicholls (8)
St Margaret Mary RC Primary School, Erdington

What Makes Me Happy

I like to make stuff,
It is fun.
I love going to the pool,
Star City is the best.
Laser tag is amazing,
I always go WHSmiths.
But my family is best,
They always love me,
With them, I am always happy!

Shay Ward (10)
St Margaret Mary RC Primary School, Erdington

This Is Me

This is me with responsibilities,
I can achieve what I want to be,
I have responsibilities.
I am Africa,
I love my family,
My family treats my friends like family.
My friends treat my family like friends.

Eugenie Diouf (8)
St Margaret Mary RC Primary School, Erdington

This Is Me!

A mazing at art,
M y hobby is swimming,
E ating ice cream is also my fave,
L ittle small, so not quite tall,
I have loads of friends and BFFs,
E veryone makes me smile.

Amélie McKenna (8)
St Margaret Mary RC Primary School, Erdington

What Makes Me, Me

U gonna, means

G od, we praise. I am

O n the lookout for rough play since I play football.

N eymar Jr, my favourite footballer, is a

N ice player and

A kind person.

Ugonna Onyiuke (9)
St Margaret Mary RC Primary School, Erdington

The Hursan

K ind to my friends,
A ctive all the time,
I ncredible at dancing,
T ruthful to everyone,
L oving to everyone,
Y ou can count on me,
N ever gives up.

Kaitlyn Dunne (8)
St Margaret Mary RC Primary School, Erdington

This Is Me

I am...
Dancer.
I love...
Colouring.
I am...
Friendly.
I love...
Noodles.
My favourite...
Is my family.
I am...
Pretty.
I have...
A sprinkle of happiness.

Ava Allen (9)
St Margaret Mary RC Primary School, Erdington

This Is Me Elidana!

E xplorer in the jungle,

L earn in school,

I nspiring stories,

D octor for my mom and dad,

A mazing girl,

N ice, helpful girl,

A ttentive girl.

Elidana Ablelom (8)

St Margaret Mary RC Primary School, Erdington

Charlotte's Rhyming Riddle

I'm Charlotte, I'm nine years old,
I'm kind and loving,
But I'm sometimes scared,
But sometimes sweaty,
Mostly shaky.

What am I?

Answer: Nervous.

Charlotte Mae Ogrady (9)

St Margaret Mary RC Primary School, Erdington

Things All About Grayson

I like football,
I like gaming with my dad and mates,
And I like pretend-fighting with my dad,
And I like playing with my dog, Molly,
She scratches me and licks me.

Grayson Marklew (8)
St Margaret Mary RC Primary School, Erdington

My Favourite Food

I really like pizza and mozzarella sticks,
I also like burgers, hot dogs with ketchup and
cheese.
When I'm at home I like to play Roblox and
Minecraft.

Rico Joseph (8)
St Margaret Mary RC Primary School, Erdington

This Is Me

L oving,

O n adventures always,

G enerous,

A dino expert,

N ever naughty... hee, hee, hee.

Logan Downey (8)
St Margaret Mary RC Primary School, Erdington

Bryan Poem

B rave,
R espectful,
Y oung and fearless,
A mazing,
N ever give up.

Bryan Macznik (8)
St Margaret Mary RC Primary School, Erdington

This Is Me

I am an animal lover,
I am good at pool,
I am a really good drawer,
I am really cool.

Mason Rendell
St Margaret Mary RC Primary School, Erdington

Me

I woke up at seven, then washed my face,
And ate some breakfast then I brushed my teeth.
I dressed up and went to school,
And when I came home I ate,
Then I went to the park to play football, at the weekend, with my brothers.
In the night I ate some apples and read some books,
My favourite thing is to go to school,
Play a lot, learn lots of new things.
When I grow up I want to be a doctor,
Because then I can help my dad.
I want to care about my family,
And I love my parents.

Jamil Maou (8)
St Monica's RC Primary School, Flixton

This Is Me

I love football because my dream is to be a
goalkeeper,
I want to watch Pokémon movies,
I love to play Pokémon games,
I love to try different foods,
My favourite subject is maths,
I love camping,
I love New Year because I love fireworks,
I want some friends to play with me,
I want to watch The Lion King movies,
I want to be a rock hero.

Theo Cheung (8)
St Monica's RC Primary School, Flixton

Friends Forever

Me, Amelia, Cydney, Ava and Nefeli are a gang,
We are all BFFs, play together and always hang.
They're my best friends,
But some other people depend.
We are always together,
And BFFs forever.
Me and Amelia have the same lunch,
But all of us are still a bunch.
Give me your hand,
And we will all make a band.

Darla Roberts Fitzpatrick (8)
St Monica's RC Primary School, Flixton

This Is My Life!

T urquoise is my third favourite colour,
H all'e is my favourite girl name,
I sabelle is my friend,
S wimming in the sea is fun.

I love bunnies,
S car is what people call me for short.

M e and Lily are BFFs forever,
E ating is my thing.

Scarlett Allen (8)
St Monica's RC Primary School, Flixton

All About Me

F orever my family's the best,
O range is my third favourite colour,
O ranges are delicious,
T he month of December is great,
B all games are fantastic,
A pples are scrumptious,
L uke is my brother,
L eo is my name.

Leo Kennedy (8)
St Monica's RC Primary School, Flixton

What I Do

I like apples after tea,
They give me lots of energy.
I like to party,
I do karate.
I learn the violin,
I play football, get in!
I ride my bike on sunny plays,
I read books at the end of days.

What do you do?

Ronan Leigton (7)
St Monica's RC Primary School, Flixton

This Is Me

I like to sing and go on the swing,
I like to have a seat when I can't hear a peep.
My mum is singing and the phone is ringing,
My dad is snoring and my brother is boring,
It is pouring and I'm stuck inside.

Ava Rawson (7)
St Monica's RC Primary School, Flixton

Faith

F aith is my name,

A nd I am obsessed with kittens,

I enjoy musicals and,

T he playing of video games,

H ere, I have told you my story, what about you?

Faith Boardwell (10)

St Monica's RC Primary School, Flixton

This Is Me!

I love going to basics, which is drama,
We do singing, acting and dancing.
I love my dog Bella as much as I love God,
My fabulous friends always help me when I need it.
My nana makes the best potato pie ever,
It is amazing!
My family is the most important thing to me,
I never judge people by their looks.
People sometimes call me a chatterbox,
To be honest, I am!
I love drawing, music and dogs,
I love going to London,
I am very kind,
And that is me!

Ruby Riding (9)
Wellfield Methodist & Anglican Church School, Burnley

This Is Me!

T he best food in the world is a nice cheesy pizza,
H ot summer days are the best sizzling days,
I love CR7, he is my favourite idol,
S wimming is the second-best sport to me.

I like football because you get a lot of exercise,
S ome of my friends are really polite and nice.

M e and my friends are going to Alton Towers,
E nergetic friends always get along.

Rylee Hoban (9)
Wellfield Methodist & Anglican Church School, Burnley

This Is Me

My name is Hannah, some people call me
nininainoodles,
I like to be annoying like noodles,
That's why they call me nininainoodles.
I like to be crazy and funny,
Like my family.
I love to make cake,
I love the library.
Sometimes I get left out at school,
But I never get left out of my family.
I love going on my bike,
Lazy but crazy,
I love the way that my dad goes crazy.

Hannah Reid (9)
Wellfield Methodist & Anglican Church School, Burnley

Burnley FC

B urnley is my favourite club,
U p the Clarets,
R elegation is coming,
N ever to be in the top ten,
L ose everything but still love them,
E ventually to be a top club,
Y ou hate us but we don't care.

F ootball is my sport, Burnley is my club,
C ornet is my favourite player.

Seb Smith (9)
Wellfield Methodist & Anglican Church School, Burnley

This Is Me!

T hankful for everything I have been given,
H ave the craziest friends,
I love my family,
S inging is my favourite thing to do.

I love making pom-poms for my friends and family,
S mile when people are upset.

M e and my friends have fun all the time,
E nergetic all of the time.

Sosha Derbyshire (9)
Wellfield Methodist & Anglican Church School, Burnley

Burnley FC

B urnley is who I support,
U nder the rain,
R elegation zone,
N eed a new stadium,
L ose a lot but doesn't matter,
E asy to lose but don't give up,
Y ou always laugh at us but we fight through it.

F ootball is my favourite sport,
C ornet is Burnley's best player.

Joseph Dickson (9)
Wellfield Methodist & Anglican Church School, Burnley

All About Me

T ap is my favourite type of dance,
H elping people is what I like to do,
I love to dance and sing,
S ims 4 is my favourite video game.

I love to play eat with my friends,
S pooky Halloween is here.

M y birthday is October the twenty-fourth,
E ve is one of my best friends.

Jessica Ashworth (9)
Wellfield Methodist & Anglican Church School, Burnley

This Is Me

T o be kind to everyone,
H ome school is the best,
I love football and support Leeds,
S undays I'm very lazy.

I love food and ice cream,
S ometimes I sleep in school.

M y family and best friends are the best,
E ven though I hate travelling, my favourite
holiday is Spain.

Riley Richardson (9)
Wellfield Methodist & Anglican Church School, Burnley

How To Make Me!

Ingredients:
Big books,
A slab of sleepiness,
One hundred grams of kindness, happiness and chattiness,
Pinch of love for pets.

How to make me:
Add in the big books and then a slab of sleepiness,
Give it a stir and whilst stirring add the pinch of love for pets,
Mix a bit longer, then stop.
Add the rest, then mix.

Jessie Madden (9)
Wellfield Methodist & Anglican Church School, Burnley

This Is Finley

T iny in size,
H ope I get to see England win,
I love reading,
S illiness is my middle name.

I have one brother and two sisters,
S ometimes I make my friend feel better.

M e and my friend like playing in my house,
E lephants have really long trunks.

Finley Danson (9)
Wellfield Methodist & Anglican Church School, Burnley

I Am Me!

My name is Lydia,
My favourite plant is Holly,
And sometimes I'm really quite jolly.
I wouldn't really wear a cap,
But I really do like to nap.
I'd describe myself as a dreaming dancer,
And my favourite reindeer is obviously Prancer.
I'm as small as a pea,
And I really love tea.

Lydia Gibson (9)
Wellfield Methodist & Anglican Church School, Burnley

All About Me

T all in my size,
H ave rotten habits,
I like playing games,
S ummer is my favourite season.

I love playing football,
S ome days I go dance.

M e and my friends like to play games,
E lephants I don't really like.

Georgia-May Mawson (9)

Wellfield Methodist & Anglican Church School, Burnley

This Is Me

T owards helping my family when my mum is sick,
H elpful to others,
I nsane sometimes,
S inging is my thing.

I deas all the time,
S chool is good for people.

M y name is Mimi,
E nergetic in sports.

Mimi Cedillo (9)

Wellfield Methodist & Anglican Church School, Burnley

This Is Me

T hankful for my life,
H appy for my family,
I like to play football,
S uper in football nets.

I like to eat food,
S ilent as a panther.

M anchester United fan,
E nergetic for sports.

Logan Meades (9)
Wellfield Methodist & Anglican Church School, Burnley

This Is Me

My name is Keegan,
I like football,
And I like the team Burnley,
And I like to watch Burnley.

I like to go on my PS4,
The game is FIFA 22 and I love my PS4,
And love my day,
And I love my dad and my mum.

Keegan Macrae (9)
Wellfield Methodist & Anglican Church School, Burnley

This Is Me

A kennings poem

I am a...
Footballer,
Chocolate eater,
Loving person,
Kickboxer,
Maths lover,
Energetic person,
Chatterbox,
Burnley fan,
Crazy person,
Joyful person,
Kind person.

Finnigan Walton (9)

Wellfield Methodist & Anglican Church School, Burnley

Oreo Rap

My name is Reo,
My last name is Oreo.
I love the solar system,
My life goes past as a shooting star.
I love my mum and dad,
I'm as high as a tree,
You see, I agree,
This is me.

Reo Taylor (10)
Wellfield Methodist & Anglican Church School, Burnley

I Am Good

I am good,
In every way possible,
Well is that true?

Well... am I really good?
Or am I bad?

I don't really know what I am,
I believe I am good,
But am I a big bad bee?

I can beat enemies,
So can I beat my badness?

My mind is jumbled up,
Like an incomplete puzzle,
I am a tiger,
Roaring on its enemies.

I know I can,
And know I will be good,
As good as the present I got...
I am good.

Micah Williams (10)
Winterbourne Boys' Academy, Thornton Heath

Spider-Man

I swung through the town,
And saw a beat down.
I helped the innocent,
And sort out the incident.
I stopped evil,
With a weasel.
Fight the crime,
And check the time.
My name is Spider-Man,
I ride a rider van.
So, that's the end,
So let Spider-Man attend.

Raees Auzine (10)
Winterbourne Boys' Academy, Thornton Heath